Anthony, the Great

ANCIENT FAITH
PUBLISHING
CHESTERTON, INDIANA

*To K.M. & A.D. — the most profound and eternal truths of Christianity
are naturally etched into the simple hearts, minds and souls of children.
Thank you both for being my vigilant instructors of such divine mysteries.— JS*

For Ksenia, Fedya, and Antosha —MP

Anthony, the Great
© 2019 John Sarantakis
Illustrations copyright © 2019 Michael Pjawka

PUBLISHED BY:
Ancient Faith Publishing
A division of Ancient Faith Ministries
PO Box 748
Chesterton, IN 46304

ISBN: 978-1-944967-58-1

Printed in Canada

store.ancientfaith.com

The Illustrations were made with watercolour, gouache, and pencil on hot pressed paper.

Image of Saint Anthony the Great courtesy of Legacy Icons. www.legacyicons.com

THIS IS ANTHONY.

Right now he is four fingers old, which isn't quite a full hand yet. That honor belongs to his older sister, Kiranna. At seven fingers old, she has even graduated to the other hand. Anthony informs her that even at seven fingers she is not as big as . . .

a dinosaur.

YOU SEE, sometimes Anthony likes to be called *Tony-Baloney,* just like sometimes he insists on wearing his space pajamas to church. (Papa always says no).

But most of the time—really ALL of the time—Anthony likes to remind his family of one simple truth. . .

WHEN PAPA COMPLAINED, "These are the biggest bills I have ever seen!" Anthony chimed in, **"BUT not as big as a dinosaur."**

WHEN MAMA SIGHED over the large pile of dirty clothes left to wash, Anthony comforted her:

"But NOT as big as a *dinosaur.*"

KIRANNA hadn't even finished admiring how tall her
doll castle was when she heard a familiar voice:

Not as **BIG** as a **DINOSAUR**

THIS IS MIKEY.

He's not as big as a you-know-what,

but he is Anthony's favorite toy. Anthony and Mikey

do absolutely everything together.

Mama says they are

"two peas in a pod."

Anthony doesn't know

what this means,

but he has noticed

that Mikey has been

eating more vegetables lately.

Anthony and Mikey love to go on

ADVENTURES.

They are often

fighting evil

or **wrestling**
monsters

or freeing
the yogurt
from its prison.

"This is what the yogurt wanted," Anthony says to Mikey with his mouth full.

NO MATTER WHAT the day may bring, Papa and Mama often take time to remind Anthony what it means to be an Orthodox Christian.

"We strive to love God more than anything else," says Mama. "Sometimes that means not getting or doing what we want. That can be hard. Even so, we struggle to put others before ourselves."

"Even on Thursdays?" thinks Anthony,

"or rainy days?

Or days we don't eat stuff that comes from cows?"

Anthony is exhausted by such an idea. *"Do you think saints had to struggle* **this much**?"* he asks Mikey.

DURING EVENING PRAYERS, Anthony remembered something while looking at the icons. His patron saint, St. Anthony the Great, had to struggle.

A LOT.

Mama says St. Anthony did this because **he loved God more than anything else**. Anthony wasn't sure if the saint's mother made him eat Brussels sprouts, though (a great struggle indeed).

Anthony quietly prayed that he might be more like this great saint of God.

THE NEXT MORNING was a good one
for Anthony. He finished all his eggs for
breakfast without complaining. He brushed
all his teeth without being told twice.

He even let Kiranna
play with Mikey, an event that
left his sister speechless.

"THIS ISN'T SO HARD,"

thought Anthony.

BUT HE DID find the day was full of

"tentations."

Papa says temptations are chances to

show our love for God.

Anthony did his best to remember

to be like his saint

each time he was faced

with a **struggle.**

WHEN MAMA ASKED Anthony to pick up the mess he'd left in his room, he struggled not to whine and yell back,

"No fair!"

Instead, he responded with a polite "No, thank you," gave a thumbs-up, and walked away.

Anthony was quite pleased with himself.

AFTER SOME THOUGHT,
Anthony decided it was best
to pick up his room after all,
this time struggling not
to get **angry** at
his socks for making
so much work.

Seeing his
efforts, Mama
smiled
with love
and warmth in
her heart.

WHEN KIRANNA generously shared with
Anthony half of her afternoon snack,
Anthony (who had already finished all of his)
struggled not to get upset and demand more.
Instead, he decided to kindly tell his sister that
she could "cook" him marshmallows, pancakes,
and ice cream to make it up.

"This much ice cream,"

said Anthony with outstretched arms,
"but not as much as a dinosaur.
That would hurt my tummy."

Kiranna giggled with **love** and warmth
in her **heart** as she tenderly
gave her brother a hug.

WHEN MIKEY TOLD ANTHONY he was otherwise engaged and could not help him build a huge pillow fort with a waterslide, Anthony really struggled.

He was struggling to struggle.

He wanted what he wanted
when he wanted it,
and he wanted to do
what he wanted to do
when he wanted to do it!

Even so, Anthony, remembering his prayer, decided to act like his saint. He gave Mikey a blessing for the journey ahead and a kiss on each cheek.

Mikey beamed with **love** and warmth in his **heart** as he marched away. Feeling better, Anthony went off to search for the water hose.

"MAMA TELLS ME you had quite the day," Papa said as he was tucking Anthony into bed.

"I tried to be like St. Anthony, but I couldn't find the desert."

"MY SWEET BOY, because you struggled against what you wanted, you helped your family.

I'm proud of you.

When we do these things, we imitate **Christ's sacrifice and love for us.** A love that is

bigger and greater

than anything else in the world."

AS ANTHONY LISTENED, his eyes opened.

Then he quietly whispered back,

"Papa—God's **love** is **bigger** than a dinosaur!"

With that, Papa's heart lit up with

love and **warmth**

as he kissed

his son

good night.

John Sarantakis—Author

Deacon John lives in New England with his wife, Kaleria, and his two children, Kiranna & Anthony. He attends and serves at St. Xenia Russian Orthodox Church in Methuen, MA. In his spare time, he can often be found napping, enjoying his family, or simply dreaming about dinosaurs—none were harmed in the making of this book.

Misha Pjawka—Illustrator

Having studied classical animation, Michael has always had an interest in storytelling brought to life through pictures. He often chases the pictures he likes best around the world. When not hunched over his desk, he hides out deep in the woods, camping on a lonely island in an isolated northern lake. Today he lives in Toronto, Canada.

SAINT ANTHONY

For the world (those living outside the Church) the "great" are often those who are the most powerful, the richest, the smartest, or the strongest. But St. Anthony's greatness came from a life of simplicity and quiet, hidden from the world. His greatness was his love for God and a life based entirely on that love: one of virtue, humility, and sacrifice.

Anthony was born in Egypt around the year 250. After the repose of his parents, he decided to dedicate his entire life to Christ. So he gave all his money to the poor and moved away from the city to be alone with God. What great faith Anthony must have had to give away all the comforts he had known since his youth. His new life was to be one of asceticism: intense struggle and self-denial out of love for God.

For many years, St. Anthony lived alone in the wilderness of the desert, not seeing or speaking with anyone. During that time, he faced numerous trials. The devil, jealous of St. Anthony's zeal and devotion to God, wished to defeat this great saint and sent him many temptations. Despite all this, St. Anthony never lost faith; constantly calling on our Lord in prayer, he was able to overcome the evil one and all the difficulties he faced.

Eventually, because of his great example and pure life, many others wished to be close to St. Anthony and gathered around him. He therefore became a teacher and spiritual father to a great many people. A defender of Orthodoxy and the teachings of the Church, St. Anthony planted the seed of monasticism for all future generations, inspiring countless souls on the path to salvation. He died at the age of 105, having obtained true spiritual greatness indeed!